STAR POWER

AND THE 9TH WORMHOLE

STAR POWER VOLUME ONE: STAR POWER and the 9TH WORMHOLE

Star charts adapted from charts found at hoshifuru.jp.

Portions of this book are published online at www.starpowercomic.com.

This volume collects STAR POWER and the 9TH WORMHOLE Issues #1-5, published online and in print betwe
February 2013 and July 2014.

First edition 2014

Printed in CHINA

STAR POWER

AND THE 9TH WORMHOLE

WORDS
MICHAEL TERRACCIANO

ART
GARTH GRAHAM

So one day I'm talking with Mookie. We're at this bar. Who knows what it's called. And he's going on about this Star Powered Sentinel thing. Interplanetary super guardian this and that.

And I'm like, "That's the alcoholo talking."

And his eyes are bubbling. Because, y'know, alcoholo. They might not have it in your sector because it's not exactly legal. But it's not technically illegal either. Not yet anyway. You end up with weird tech floating in your eyes. Which sounds horrible and puts off a lot of folks, but you take it in a pill and these things are small. Like a grain of sand is a mountain next to these things. So they get in there, in your eye but you don't feel it, and they're networked to beam light directly into your brain so it tricks you into being drunk. But there's nothing to metabolize so there's no hangover when it's done. Fluid dynamics from your eye's interior keep their kinetic batteries going for about an hour or two. Depends on your tolerance, I guess. And then they just get flushed out.

So yeah, Star Powered Sentinels. It's nonsense, right? Mookie's all, "No, no, man. Seriously." And he starts up again. Galactic civilization, and golden age, and void things.

And I'm, like, "It's 3009. Space isn't an adventure. Space is for omnigarchs and ultracorps. The rest of us gotta worry about how we're gonna pay for tomorrow's nutrient pack."

And he's like, "Space isn't theirs. They took the idea of it from us. But its ours. We need to take it back."

But, y'know, whatever. Alcoholo makes you say big crazy ideas. Like, last time we were out like this I couldn't shut up about an AI platform that seeks out and corrects malignant applications of emergent technologies. I mean, how bad is that? Robot Accountant: The Action Movie. He doesn't even tease me about it anymore, so I can't hold it against him if he's talking about space like it's some kind of birthright.

Now here it is, 3014, and Mookie's scrounged up this artomatic he keeps calling GARTH and they've made a hell of a thing out of this Star Powered Sentinel idea. Guess he showed me.

Brian Clevinger is a semi-automatic collection of proteins suspended in water that is older than the Sun.

The birth of Star Power was much like the birth of a star: it took a long time, and it came from very humble beginnings.

Star Power began as Captain Space, a series of LiveJournal entries I made in the middle of the night. Brian Clevinger was doing something similar with Atomic Robo, and I had been inspired by his prose. Atomic Robo was eventually turned into a comic book, but Captain Space sat on my hard drive as I continued work on my webcomic, "Dominic Deegan: Oracle for Hire."

I paid little attention to Captain Space until my friend began publishing an independent magazine called "Spwug." She asked me to contribute something creative, so I found my Captain Space pieces and submitted them. For a few months, the adventures of Captain Space were published in Spwug. That project eventually ended, and Captain Space went into stasis once again.

As Dominic Deegan neared its end, I began to consider my next project. I returned to my old Captain Space entries. I converted those short stories into a five-part script called "Captain Space and the Galaxy's Most Wanted." It featured such familiar villains as the Void Angels, Black Hole Bill, and Countess Nurak-Nor of the Ninth Wormhole. It was a classic sci-fi space adventure, full of starship battles, laser fights, and two-fisted brawls amongst the stars.

But I needed someone to draw this new comic. My own artwork wasn't going to do the trick. I approached Garth, a longtime friend of mine in the webcomics world, with the idea for Captain Space. He liked it, but was busy with his own webcomic, "Finder's Keepers." The very talented Dirk Tiede did some design sketches for me, but his own projects also took precedence and he politely declined any further involvement. I feared Captain Space would be returning to stasis.

Brian Clevinger was nice enough to read the script, and liked it so much that he pitched it to his publisher. Thinking I had an "in" to the world of print comics, I approached Garth again, armed with this information. Now he was willing to look at the script, which he liked very much and signed on to the project. But, as with so many things in the world of print comics, things didn't work out and Captain Space never took off.

Garth had faith in the project and stuck with me. We sat down with it again and really examined it. We were big fans of the Most Wanted: Black Hole Bill, the Void Angels, Countess Nurak-Nor. Captain Space himself was another matter. He was a classic sci-fi hero, but he wasn't as interesting as his villains. So we decided to rework the script from the ground up, at which point I made a pitch to Garth I knew I would have to work hard to sell him on.

"Let's turn it into a superhero comic."

He was hesitant. Garth loved superheroes, but didn't enjoy things like "the superhero community," where super-powered beings are everywhere and getting into increasingly overpowered fights with one another. This was also the time of a company's infamous reboot, where a gross majority of female superheroes were becoming figureheads for causes and/or just plain sex objects. Modern superheroes were not what he remembered them to be, and he was hesitant to associate himself with a genre he wasn't enjoying any more.

I asked him how he would feel if our main character was the only superhero in our universe, and if we changed the former Captain Space to a female protagonist.

His reply was, "I'm listening."

The script that would become Star Power became a truly collaborative project after that. Ideas were bounced back-and-forth until a new concept was formed. For example, I wanted a classic superhero costume. Garth did not (though I've only just discovered that he had sketched some designs, the sneak). Garth wanted a futuristic armor idea that showed a respectable amount of skin. I did not. We offered one another different compromises until a costume began to take shape. The examples of this process are in the sketchbook section of this book, and the result is the design you see today.

But the real beauty of our partnership was that there was little convincing to be done. We both discovered we wanted the very same things out of a sci-fi superhero book: a strong female protagonist who has the potential to be sexy without being sexualized; a setting that celebrates the wonder of space and the boundless imagination of science fiction; a story that has more action than violence, and more adventure than angst.

The only thing I had to really sell to him was the name itself. Star Power. He was reluctant to commit to a name that was a pun on celebrity influence, but he eventually came around.

We love Star Power. We believe in it. And when it launched, it was very well received. We were happy to discover that there were many others who were looking for the same things in a superhero story. We met fathers who told us this was the sort of story they could share with their daughters to get them into comics. We met women who took one look at Danica's design and simply said, "thank you." We met bright-eyed kids who saw the wonder of superpowers, and it was the same look we had had when we were young.

Star Power and the Ninth Wormhole was not an ambitious project. We did not set out to remake the wheel or reinvent the comics medium. We did not think we were visionaries who were out to shatter all preconceptions about superheroes. We simply set out to make the comics we wanted to see, and have fun doing it. People seemed to enjoy the ride so far, and their support for our journey has made this book possible.

Will things get more ambitious and visionary in the future? We have no idea. But we hope you come along for the adventure, Star Powered or otherwise.

-Michael Terracciano

CHAPTER ONE

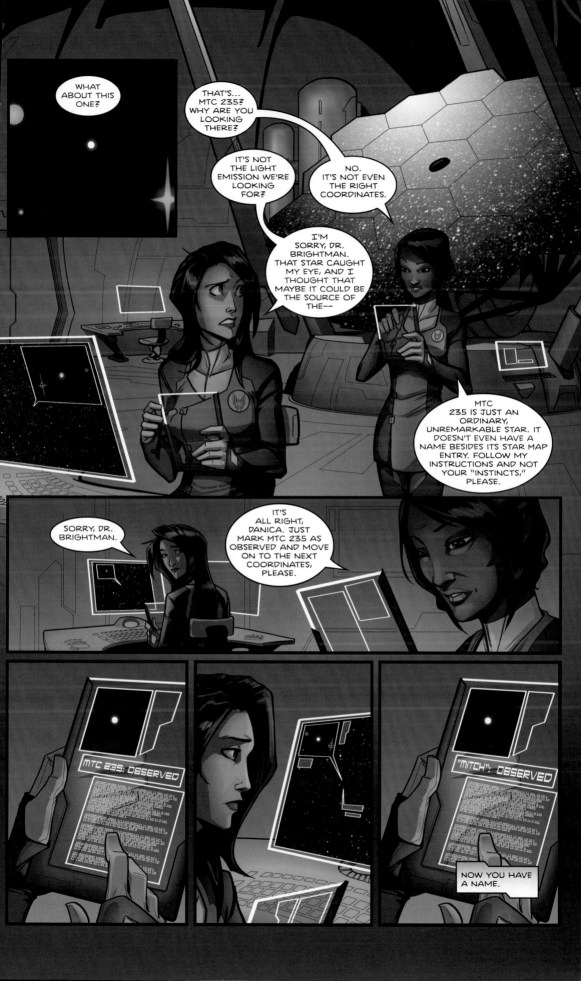

SIR! THE STATION IS UNDER ATTACK!

I'M AWARE OF THAT *NOW!* WHY WEREN'T WE AWARE OF THIS *BEFORE* THEY OPENED FIRE?

IT'S THE VOID ANGELS, SIR! THEIR STEALTH-TECH MUST HAVE GOTTEN THEM PAST OUR PERIMETER SCANNERS!

SCRAMBLE THE DEFENSE DROIDS AND GIVE ME A DAMAGE REPORT!

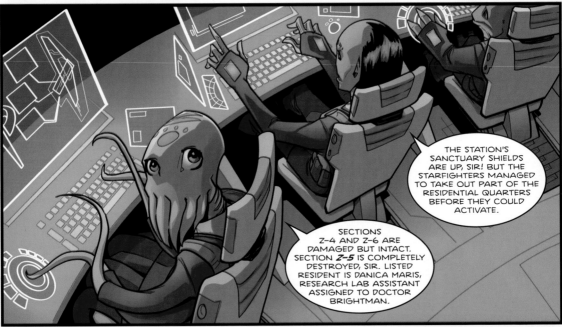

THE STATION'S SANCTUARY SHIELDS ARE UP, SIR! BUT THE STARFIGHTERS MANAGED TO TAKE OUT PART OF THE RESIDENTIAL QUARTERS BEFORE THEY COULD ACTIVATE.

SECTIONS Z-4 AND Z-6 ARE DAMAGED BUT INTACT. SECTION *Z-5* IS COMPLETELY DESTROYED, SIR. LISTED RESIDENT IS DANICA MARIS, RESEARCH LAB ASSISTANT ASSIGNED TO DOCTOR BRIGHTMAN.

"PERSONNEL LOGS INDICATE SHE WAS *IN* THE ROOM WHEN IT WAS HIT."

GET THE REPAIR BOTS WORKING ON Z-4 AND Z-6, AND SET THE DEFENSE DROIDS TO OFFENSIVE PARAMETER 7.

I WANT THOSE STARFIGHTERS TAKEN OUT BEFORE THEY KILL ANYONE ELSE.

SLOW DOWN. TAKE A DEEP BREATH. REALIZE WHAT'S JUST HAPPENED TO YOU.

YOU JUST FOUGHT OFF THE VOID ANGELS. SOME OF THE NASTIEST SCUM THIS SIDE OF THE GALAXY.

YOU. JUST. FOUGHT. THEM. OFF. BY *YOURSELF.*

AND YOU DID IT OUT IN SPACE. *WITHOUT* A SPACE SUIT. WITHOUT ANY *LIFE SUPPORT.*

DANICA. YOU ARE IN *SPACE.*

WOW.

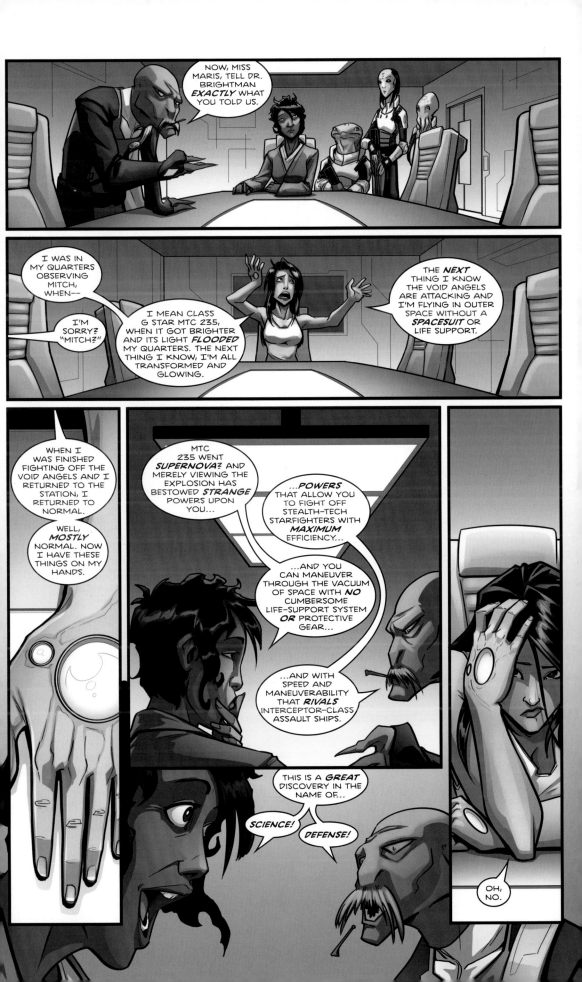

"UNBELIEVABLE. MTC 235 IS *GONE*. NO SUPERNOVA REMNANT. NO TRACE OF IT AT ALL. FOR IT TO ALTOGETHER VANISH LIKE THIS IS..."

"UNBELIEVABLE!"

"YES. THANK YOU, DANICA."

IT STANDS TO REASON THAT MTC 235--

MITCH.

YES, "MITCH," WAS NOT A STAR AT ALL. WHATEVER IT WAS, IT MUST BE RESIDING IN THESE STRANGE DISCS AND GIVING YOU THESE POWERS.

IF MITCH WASN'T A STAR, THEN WHAT WAS IT?

AN EXCELLENT QUERY, STAR POWERED SENTINEL. ALLOW ME TO SHED SOME LIGHT ON THE SUBJECT.

AAAAAAAH!

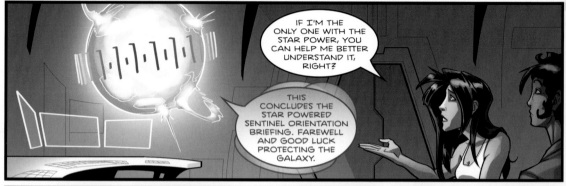

CHAPTER TWO

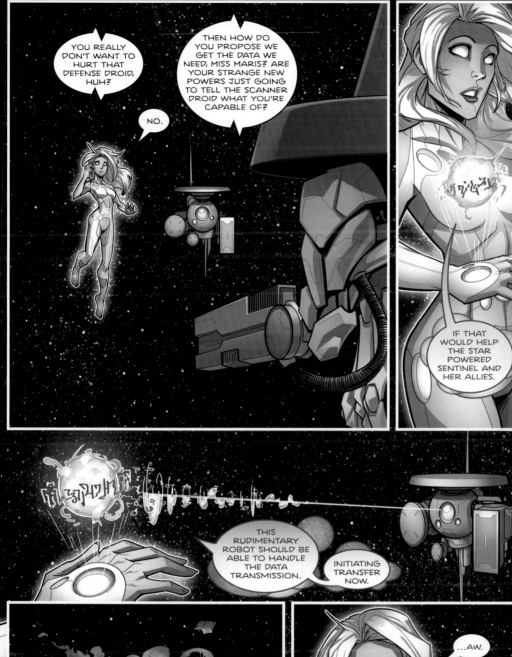

YOU REALLY DON'T WANT TO HURT THAT DEFENSE DROID, HUH?

NO.

THEN HOW DO YOU PROPOSE WE GET THE DATA WE NEED, MISS MARIS? ARE YOUR STRANGE NEW POWERS JUST GOING TO TELL THE SCANNER DROID WHAT YOU'RE CAPABLE OF?

IF THAT WOULD HELP THE STAR POWERED SENTINEL AND HER ALLIES.

THIS RUDIMENTARY ROBOT SHOULD BE ABLE TO HANDLE THE DATA TRANSMISSION.

INITIATING TRANSFER NOW.

...AW.

PERHAPS I SAID TOO MUCH.

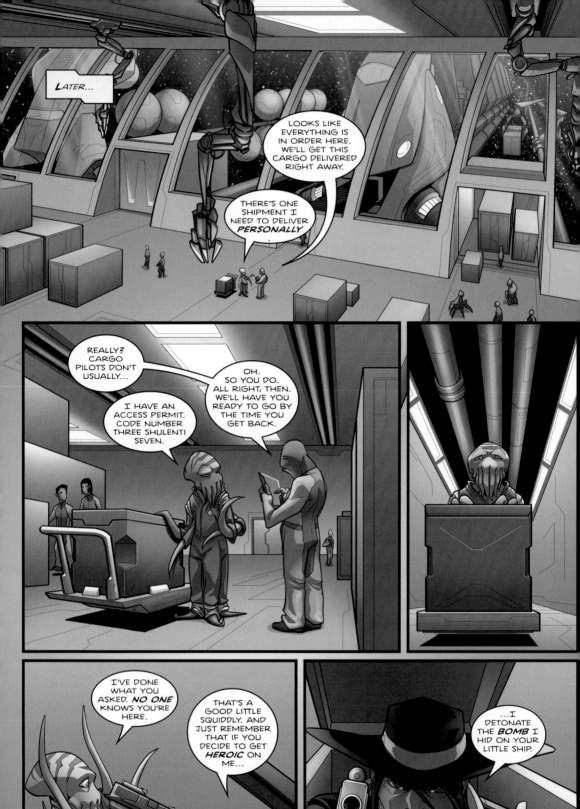

LATER...

LOOKS LIKE EVERYTHING IS IN ORDER HERE. WE'LL GET THIS CARGO DELIVERED RIGHT AWAY.

THERE'S ONE SHIPMENT I NEED TO DELIVER *PERSONALLY*

REALLY? CARGO PILOTS DON'T USUALLY...

OH. SO YOU DO. ALL RIGHT, THEN. WE'LL HAVE YOU READY TO GO BY THE TIME YOU GET BACK.

I HAVE AN ACCESS PERMIT. CODE NUMBER THREE SHULENTI SEVEN.

I'VE DONE WHAT YOU ASKED. *NO ONE* KNOWS YOU'RE HERE.

THAT'S A GOOD LITTLE SQUIDDLY. AND JUST REMEMBER THAT IF YOU DECIDE TO GET *HEROIC* ON ME...

...I DETONATE THE *BOMB* I HID ON YOUR LITTLE SHIP.

THAT *HURT?* THAT WAS JUST A *WARM-UP.* NOW LET'S SEE HOW BAD THE REAL NASTY AMMO HURTS YA.

YOU SHINE *REAL* BRIGHT, SWEETHEART...

...BUT EVERY LIGHT BURNS OUT *EVENTUALLY.*

ARGH!

ZAP!

SANCTUARY SIX SECURITY. STAND *DOWN,* OR THE NEXT SHOT WILL HURT A *LOT* MORE.

Gotcha.

YEAH? STAND *THIS.*

CLICK

CLICK CLICK CLICK CLICK

...THE *ZUCK* IS WRONG WITH THIS DETONATOR?

THWACK

GUH!

RESTRAIN HIM BEFORE HE GETS UP AGAIN. I WANT THAT *MANIAC* LOCKED UP.

YOU SAVED MY LIFE. THANK YOU, *WHOEVER* YOU ARE.

IT WAS NOTHING. I'M...THAT IS, I'M A STAR-POWERED--

SHE'LL HAVE TIME FOR QUESTIONS LATER. RIGHT *NOW*, SHE NEEDS TO COME WITH *US*.

DID SHE SAY HER NAME WAS *STAR POWER*?

CHAPTER THREE

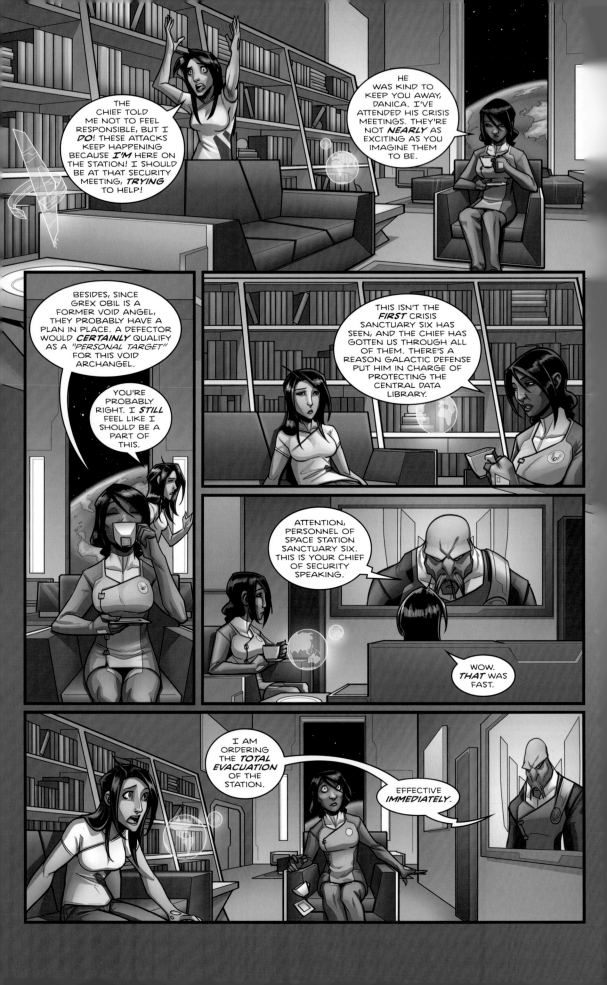

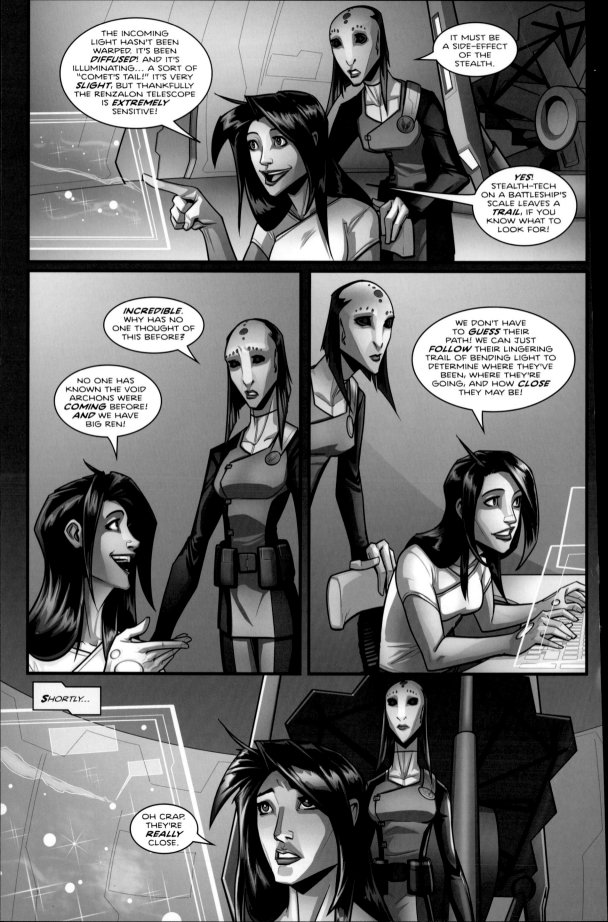

SHOULD WE RESUME THE DATA DISPERSAL, CHIEF?

GO GET 'EM, STAR POWER!

NO. GET TO *BATTLE STATIONS.*

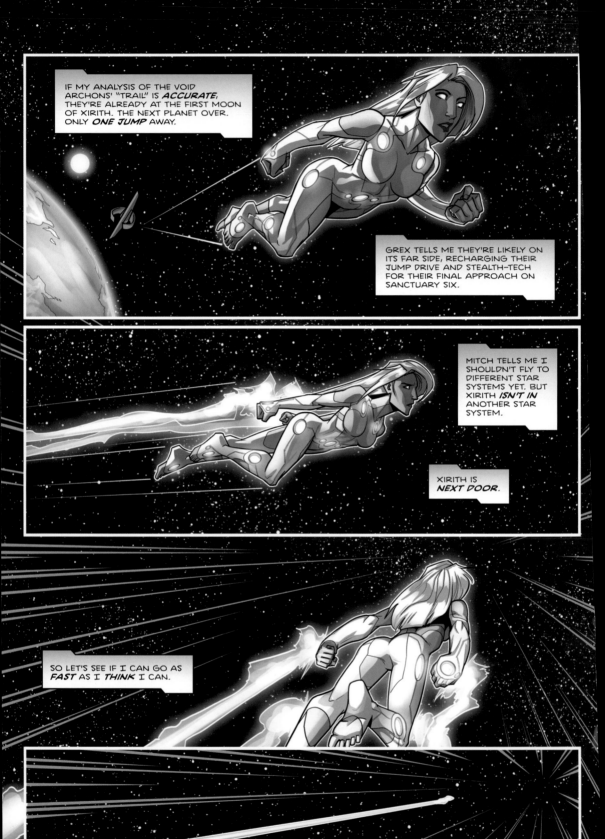

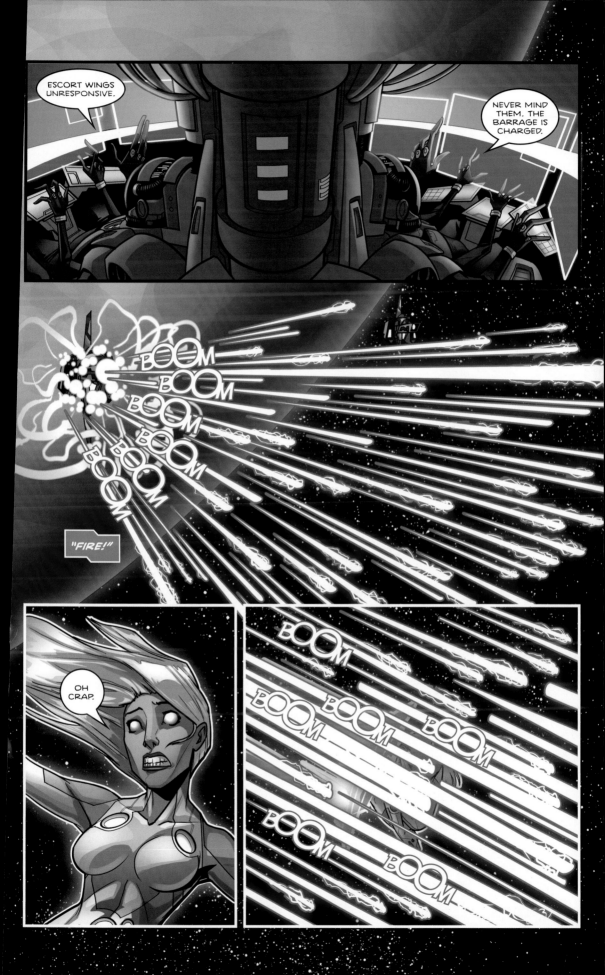

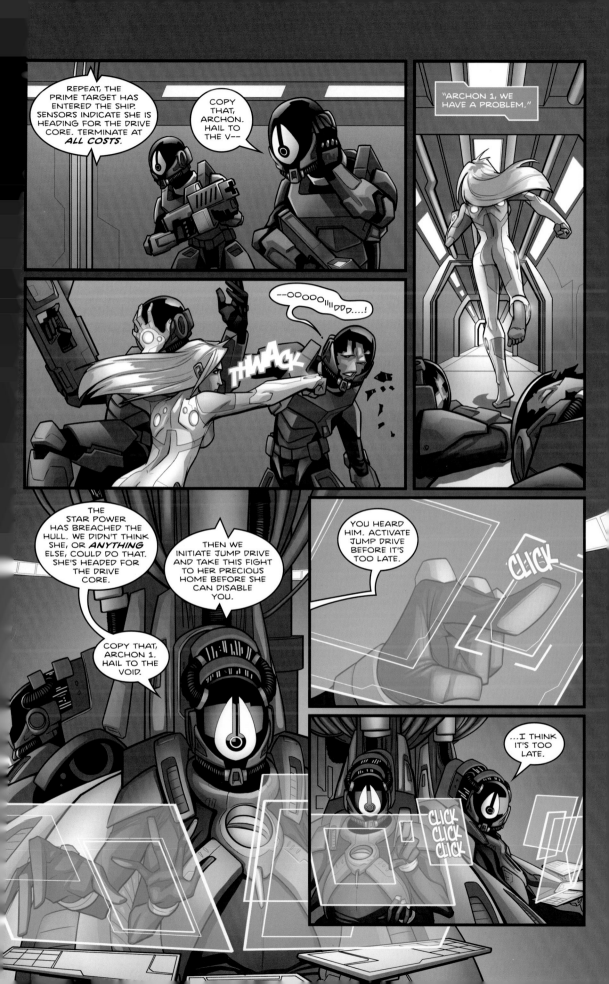

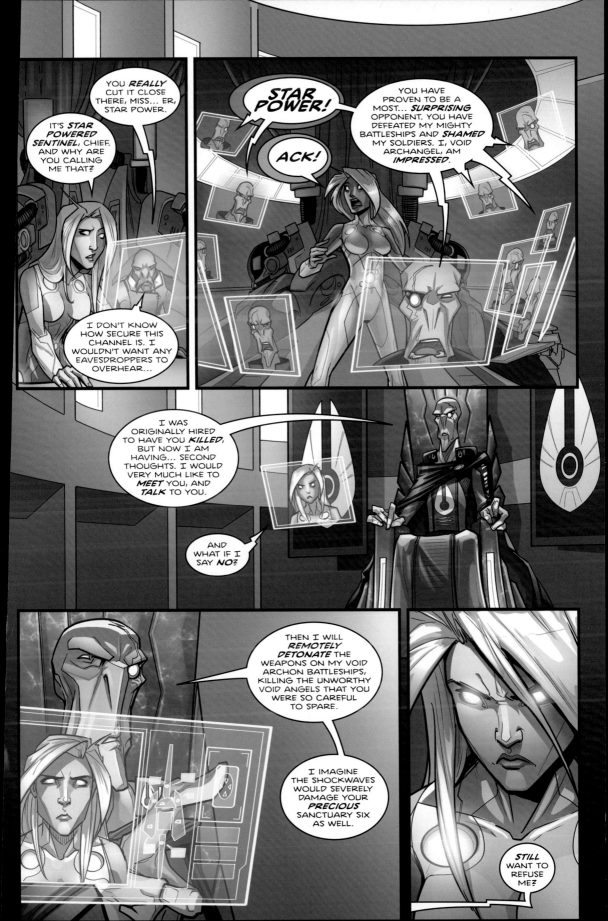

CHAPTER FOUR

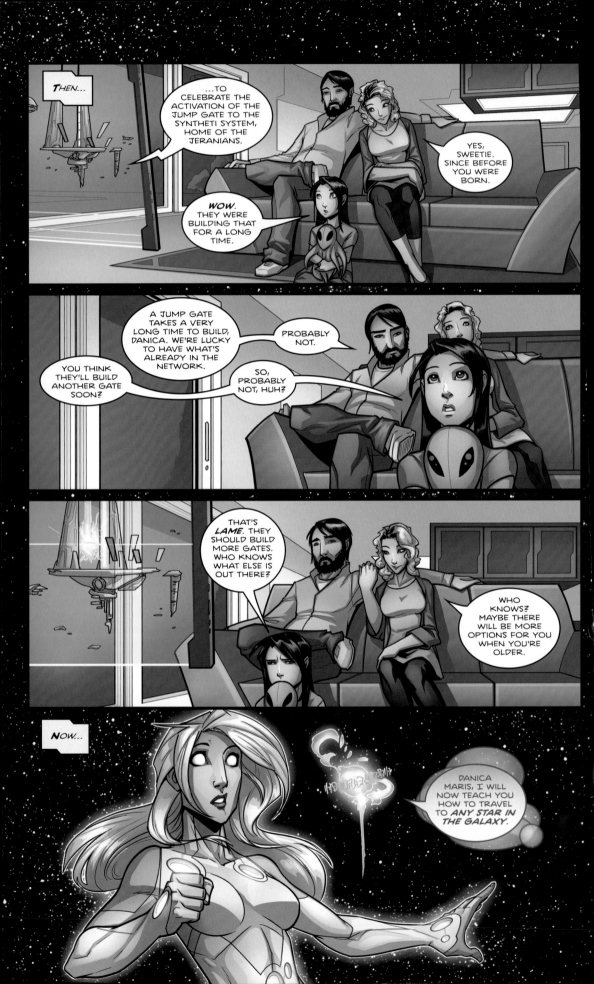

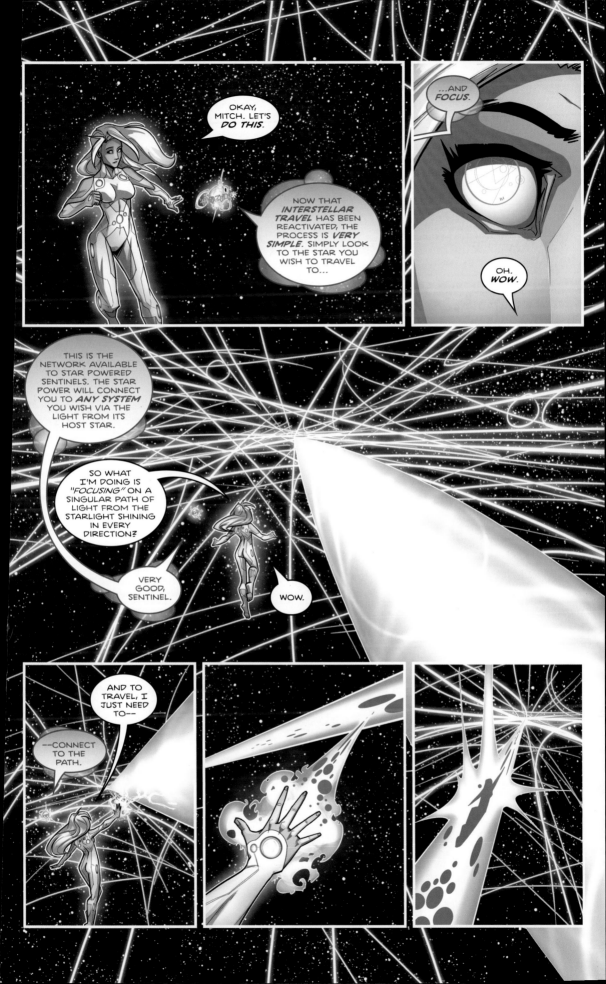

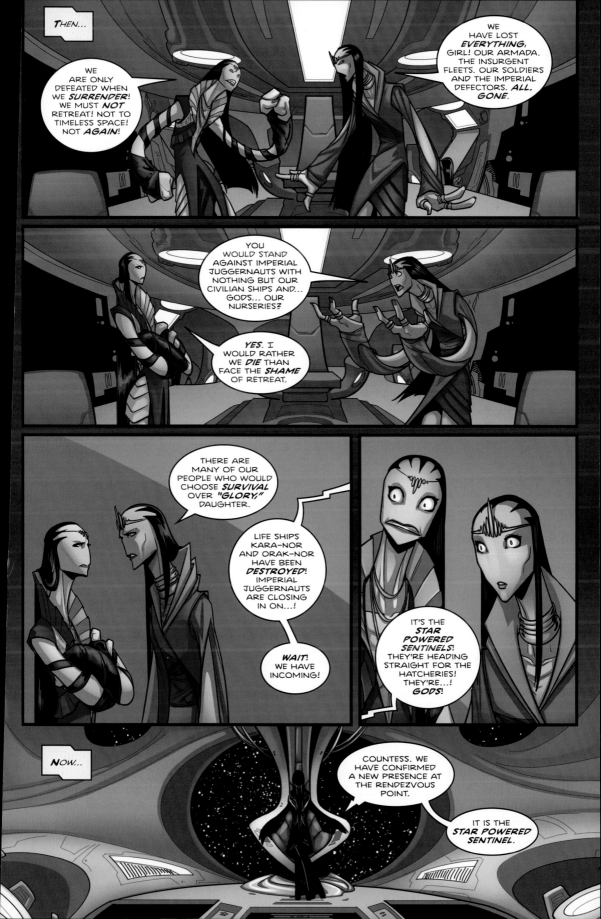

THEN...

WE ARE ONLY DEFEATED WHEN WE *SURRENDER!* WE MUST *NOT* RETREAT! NOT TO TIMELESS SPACE! NOT *AGAIN!*

WE HAVE LOST *EVERYTHING,* GIRL! OUR ARMADA. THE INSURGENT FLEETS. OUR SOLDIERS AND THE IMPERIAL DEFECTORS. *ALL. GONE.*

YOU WOULD STAND AGAINST IMPERIAL JUGGERNAUTS WITH NOTHING BUT OUR CIVILIAN SHIPS AND... GODS... OUR NURSERIES?

YES. I WOULD RATHER WE *DIE* THAN FACE THE *SHAME* OF RETREAT.

THERE ARE MANY OF OUR PEOPLE WHO WOULD CHOOSE *SURVIVAL* OVER *"GLORY,"* DAUGHTER.

LIFE SHIPS KARA-NOR AND ORAK-NOR HAVE BEEN *DESTROYED!* IMPERIAL JUGGERNAUTS ARE CLOSING IN ON...!

WAIT! WE HAVE INCOMING!

IT'S THE *STAR POWERED SENTINELS!* THEY'RE HEADING STRAIGHT FOR THE HATCHERIES! THEY'RE...! *GODS!*

NOW...

COUNTESS. WE HAVE CONFIRMED A NEW PRESENCE AT THE RENDEZVOUS POINT.

IT IS THE *STAR POWERED SENTINEL.*

SENSORS ARE LIGHTING UP. TARGET IS INCOMING.

GOOD.

HOW DID YOU FIND ME SO SOON AFTER I...?

I'LL BE THE ONE ASKING THE QUESTIONS, STAR POWER. YOU'RE HERE TO TALK ON MY TERMS, REMEMBER?

ALL RIGHT, THEN. ASK AWAY.

I'LL ALSO BE THE ONE GIVING THE ORDERS. UNLESS YOU WANT ME TO KILL ALL THOSE PEOPLE YOU WORKED SO HARD TO SAVE.

YOU GOT HERE QUICKLY.

FUNNY. I SAID THE SAME THING WHEN YOUR GOONS BLEW UP MY ROOM.

OUR INTERCEPTORS ARE AMONG THE FASTEST STARFIGHTERS IN THE GALAXY. REACHING TARGETS QUICKLY IS WHAT WE DO.

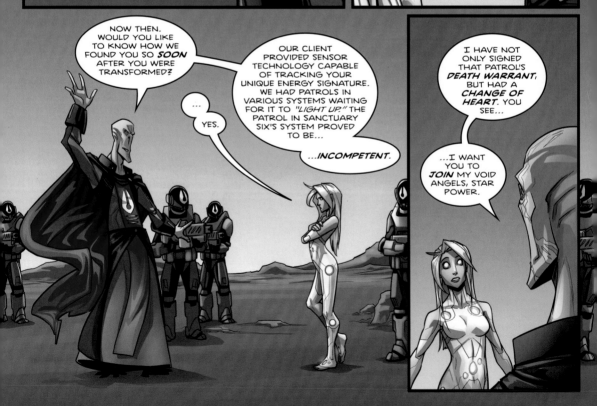

NOW THEN. WOULD YOU LIKE TO KNOW HOW WE FOUND YOU SO SOON AFTER YOU WERE TRANSFORMED?

OUR CLIENT PROVIDED SENSOR TECHNOLOGY CAPABLE OF TRACKING YOUR UNIQUE ENERGY SIGNATURE. WE HAD PATROLS IN VARIOUS SYSTEMS WAITING FOR IT TO "LIGHT UP." THE PATROL IN SANCTUARY SIX'S SYSTEM PROVED TO BE...

... YES.

...INCOMPETENT.

I HAVE NOT ONLY SIGNED THAT PATROL'S DEATH WARRANT, BUT HAD A CHANGE OF HEART. YOU SEE...

...I WANT YOU TO JOIN MY VOID ANGELS, STAR POWER.

SCANNER AND DEFENSE DROIDS HAVE FINISHED THEIR SWEEP OF THE VOID ARCHON BATTLESHIP, CHIEF. THEY FOUND VARIOUS DETONATION DEVICES.

GREAT GALAXY. WHAT IS IT WITH THESE MANIACS AND DETONATORS?

FURTHERMORE, IT APPEARS THE PILOTS AND CREW DIDN'T KNOW ABOUT THESE PARTICULAR FEATURES OF THEIR SHIP.

HOW CONVENIENT OF THEIR BOSS TO LEAVE THEM OUT OF THE JOB DESCRIPTION.

CAN THE DEFENSE DROIDS DISARM THEM? IF THAT WEAPONRY BLOWS, WE'RE LOOKING AT SERIOUS DAMAGE TO THE STATION, AND LOSS OF LIFE.

REPORTS INDICATE THAT THE DEVICES ARE OF GRAIDANI DESIGN.

SO THE DROIDS CAN'T TOUCH THEM.

NO, SIR. IT'S BEEN DETERMINED THAT THEY MUST BE MANUALLY DISARMED.

REPORTING FOR DUTY, CHIEF.

HAS THIS INFORMATION BEEN PASSED TO THE NECESSARY PERSONNEL?

YES, SIR. KAYLO'S ALREADY SUITED UP.

YOU MONSTER!

SSSSHHHBRRAAAK!

FWEEEN!

GET AWAY FROM ME!

OH NO. OH, NO... NO NO NO.

I... I KILLED A...

...A ROBOT?!

AAAAAAH!!

SSSSZZZZZZZTTT!!!

CHAPTER FIVE

EARLIER...

THIS IS GALACTIC DEFENSE SHIP *ALCOR*. COME IN, SPACE STATION SANCTUARY SIX.

THIS IS SANCTUARY SIX. GO ON, *ALCOR*.

WE'VE FOUND THE SOURCE OF THAT SIGNAL. IT'S THE VOID ANGEL FLAGSHIP. WHAT'S *LEFT* OF IT AND ITS CREW.

THERE ARE BODIES *EVERYWHERE*. WHOEVER WASN'T SPACED WAS *RIPPED* APART.

ALCOR, DID YOUR SCANNERS FIND ANY SIGN OF SANCTUARY SIX LAB ASSISTANT *DANICA MARIS?* IS SHE AMONG THE...?

NEGATIVE, BUT AMONG THE DEAD ARE THE REMAINS OF ROBOT UNITS *UNIDENTIFIABLE* BY GALACTIC DEFENSE DATA BANKS.

WE ALSO PICKED UP A *STRANGE ENERGY SIGNATURE*. WE COMPARED OUR FINDINGS TO THE *MIZAR'S*. THEY DETECTED THE *SAME* ENERGY NEAR *XIRITH*.

SANCTUARY SIX, DO YOU HAVE ANY *RELEVANT* INFORMATION REGARDING THIS? IT MAY LEAD US TO YOUR MISSING LAB ASSISTANT.

YES. UPLOADING ALL OUR INFORMATION ON THE ENERGY SIGNATURE CODE-NAMED: *STAR POWER*.

THAT'S WHY MITCH HAS BEEN SO QUIET ABOUT THE NINTH WORM HOLE. THE STAR POWERED SENTINELS WERE *YOUR* ENFORCERS.

YOU WERE *MEANT* TO BE, UNTIL A GROUP OF *RADICALS* STOLE WHAT WAS TO BE OUR GREATEST WEAPON AND *WARPED* IT INTO YOUR... *STAR POWER.*

THEIR BELIEFS WERE HERETICAL. *"MERCY* AND *COMPASSION* FOR THE *LESSER RACES."* *Bah.* THEY SPREAD THE STAR POWER, LIKE A *DISEASE,* AMONG THE PLANETS WE HAD *RIGHTFULLY ENSLAVED* DURING THE FIRST WORMHOLE.

THE SENTINELS DROVE MY PEOPLE BACK UNTIL WE HAD *NOWHERE TO GO* BUT TIMELESS SPACE, WHERE EONS PASS... BUT *NOT* FOR THOSE TRAVELING WITHIN IT.

TIMELESS SPACE. DOES SHE MEAN... *TIME DILATION?*

EVERY TIME WE RETURNED AS A NEW WORMHOLE TO *RECLAIM* OUR *RIGHTFUL PLACE* AS RULERS... THERE *YOU* WERE, OUR ANCIENT ENEMIES. *DRIVING US BACK* INTO TIMELESS SPACE. *TAUNTING* US THROUGH THE PASSING MILLENNIA.

IT MUST BE. HER PEOPLE'S LAST RESORT WAS TO ESCAPE AT THE SPEED OF LIGHT.

UNTIL, *AT LAST,* THE HERESY THAT BUILT YOUR ORDER CAUSED THE *NEAR EXTERMINATION* OF MY PEOPLE.

MERCY AND *COMPASSION* CAUSED THE...? HOW IS THAT *POSSIBLE?*

SILENCE, SENTINEL! YOU DO *NOT* GET ANY MORE ANSWERS...

...BEFORE YOU *DIE.*

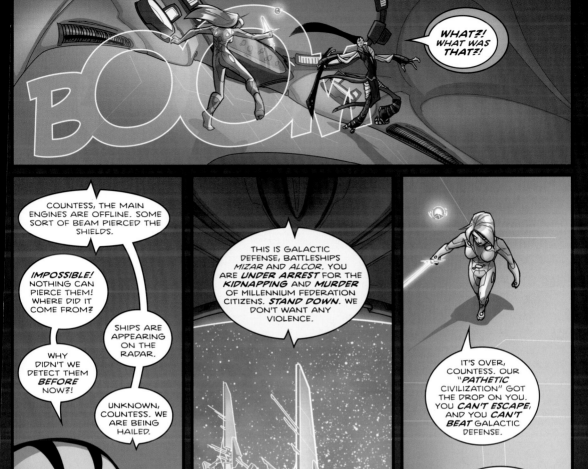

WHAT?! WHAT WAS THAT?!

COUNTESS, THE MAIN ENGINES ARE OFFLINE. SOME SORT OF BEAM PIERCED THE SHIELDS.

IMPOSSIBLE! NOTHING CAN PIERCE THEM! WHERE DID IT COME FROM?

WHY DIDN'T WE DETECT THEM *BEFORE* NOW?!

SHIPS ARE APPEARING ON THE RADAR.

UNKNOWN, COUNTESS. WE ARE BEING HAILED.

THIS IS GALACTIC DEFENSE, BATTLESHIPS *MIZAR* AND *ALCOR.* YOU ARE *UNDER ARREST* FOR THE *KIDNAPPING* AND *MURDER* OF MILLENNIUM FEDERATION CITIZENS. *STAND DOWN.* WE DON'T WANT ANY VIOLENCE.

IT'S OVER, COUNTESS. OUR *"PATHETIC* CIVILIZATION" GOT THE DROP ON YOU. YOU *CAN'T ESCAPE,* AND YOU *CAN'T BEAT* GALACTIC DEFENSE.

YOU DARE SUGGEST YOU'RE... *SUPERIOR?* YOU DARE SUGGEST I... *SURRENDER?*

I AM A SCINTILLIAN *MATRIARCH!* THE *PINNACLE* OF MY PEOPLE! WE *FIGHT* UNTIL WE *DIE!*

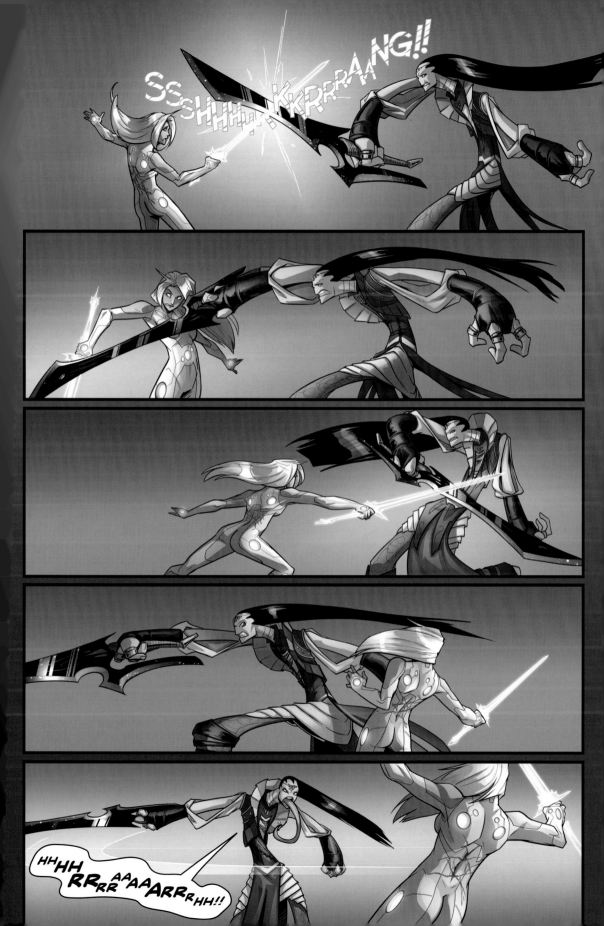

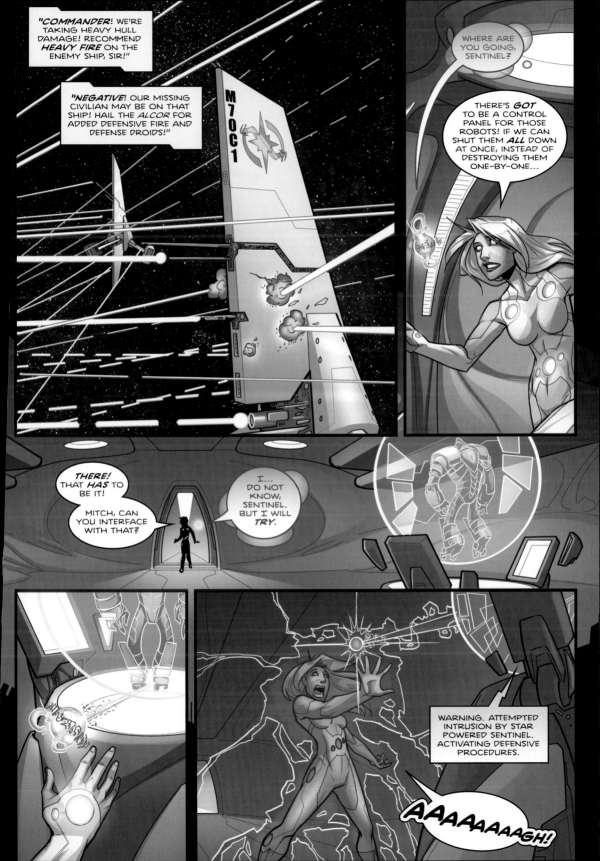

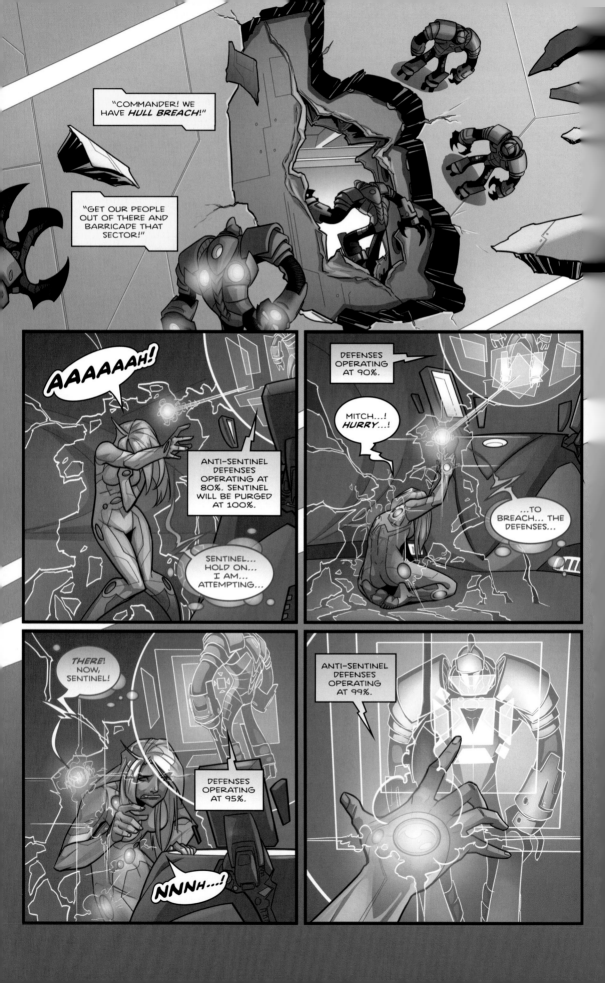

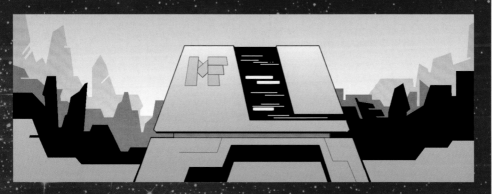

There are not precisely one thousand worlds comprising the Millennium Federation. There are many, many more. The "thousand worlds" is in reference to the thousand home worlds of the thousand major races comprising the Federation. For example, Humans have a presence on every planet in the Sol system, but that does not count for eight Human worlds, nor the various human colonies and settlements on other worlds in other systems. Earth, the home world and central seat of local government, is the one accounted for in the official numbers.

There is a central set of laws and rules that governs all the worlds of the Millennium Federation. They are not numerous, but they are strictly enforced: acceptance, protection, freedom, and justice for all who live within the Millennium Federation. The laws and rules of the specific thousand worlds are otherwise left to the local governments to enforce, such as legal drinking and voting ages, procedures for marriages (if applicable), and anything else that does not conflict with the Federation's ideals. No one is forced to be as communal as a Shulentin, nor as orderly as a Zairakian.

Galactic Defense is the Millennium Federation's "standing army," though with little threat of war from outside the Federation (for now), G.D. is also an acting police force. There are certainly bad apples and the occasional corrupt officer, but on the whole Galactic Defense is a well-respected organization, which is quite an accomplishment given its size.

The Millennium Federation holds regular meetings in the Millennium Hall, which is not a fixed location but simply a name for the gathering of the thousand races' representatives. There is one ambassador from each race, speaking on behalf of their world's government. Matters of galactic import are discussed and reports are filed. The meetings are for maintenance, not intrigue, and Millennium Hall gatherings are far less exciting than some movies would have people believe.

All in all, the Millennium Federation is exactly what it appears to be: an honest attempt at a peaceful and tolerant galactic civilization. With the rest of the unexplored galaxy having descended into relative barbarism and petty wars since the Eighth Wormhole, the Federation is a positive influence and worth protecting.

Sanctuary Six orbits the planet Alpel in the Lis system. Alpel, like Gioren and Liashanti, are unsettled "garden worlds" where animal and plant life thrive. The Millennium Federation forbids any contact or interference with these burgeoning worlds, treating them as planetary wildlife reserves. Sanctuary Six has numerous teams of scientists studying the flora and fauna of these gardens.

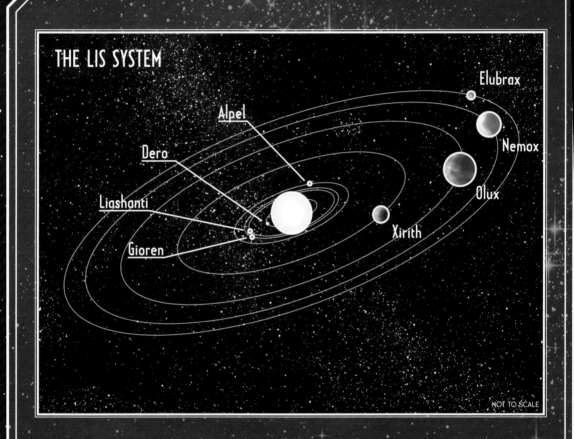

THE LIS SYSTEM

Elubrax

Alpel

Dero

Nemox

Liashanti

Olux

Gioren

Xirith

NOT TO SCALE

Sanctuary Six is not the only research station of its kind in the Millennium Federation. There are ten in total, all with their own Central Data Libraries, though with different names (see: Prime Archive, First Collection, etc). They are all located in "garden world systems" for minimum interference with busy Federation life.

The purpose of ten separate secluded research stations, all with separate Central Data Libraries, is twofold.

1) To keep valuable knowledge spread out instead of centrally located. That way, in the case of the Millennium Federation's decline and/or downfall, scientific advancement cannot be wiped out in one terrible stroke. There are many, many other libraries and research facilities in the Federation, but the Sanctuary Stations are the biggest.

2) There are many, many aspiring scientists and researchers in the Millennium Federation. Having ten diverse and thriving research sanctuaries helps accommodate the numbers of a galactic civilization.

Each station is governed by the same set of Federation rules, but each has its own "character" to it, much like cities or large universities on Earth.

SPACE STATION SANCTUARY SIX

Historians adore Humans. To the people of the Millennium Federation, their story is one of the most fascinating in all of galactic history. They have been the focus of many documentaries and award-winning dramas.

When the Humans were discovered by the Millennium Federation, they were already a star-faring

people. They had colonized their inner planets and the moons of their outer gas giants. Yet their journey to the stars was not in the name of progress. It was in the name of war.

Humans were divided into two warring factions: United Crusade and Children of Earth. The origin of their conflict was vast and complicated, but the result was all too familiar to Humans: War, across an entire solar system.

The Millennium Federation had never seen a race fighting itself on such a massive scale. It decided to take action. The Millennium Federation's prevailing theory was that the introduction of an outside presence would force the Humans to unite. Galactic Defense Diplomacy Ships announced their impending arrival to the warring factions. What happened next shocked the Federation.

The divided Humans could not agree on how to confront the "invading" ships, and so the fighting intensified. When Galactic Defense ships finally arrived in the Sol system under a banner of peace, Humans were still killing Humans, but on an even greater scale. Convinced these warlike people were doomed to slaughter themselves to extinction, the Millennium Federation made plans to leave the barbaric Humans to their fate.

Then a coalition of rebels from both sides of the conflict, weary of constant war, appealed to the Federation. They called themselves United Earth.

United Earth desperately sought an end to the perpetual cycle of war that plagued the Human race. The Millennium Federation could not deny their call for help, and so began one of the most ambitious projects in galactic history. The Millennium Federation did not directly interfere with Human politics, but rather counseled United Earth in interplanetary diplomacy. Word of the Federation's advanced technology and inclusive society was spread through the efforts of United Earth peacekeepers. Slowly, a glimmer of hope gained momentum among the weary Humans: an end to war, and the beginning of a new golden age among the stars.

It was not a quick or easy process. It took generations. All the while, the Millennium Federation observed, counseled, and recorded the new path of the Human race. After two centuries of struggle, the Federation's patience paid off. The Humans united, in peace.

United Earth rose from the ashes of war like a phoenix (see: Human mythology). Borders were dissolved. Peace treaties were written. Blasted planetary environments were restored. A unified government was established. Humans were, at long last, one people.

Their struggle had been well-documented by the Millennium Federation, and Humans were welcomed by the established worlds with open arms. For their part, Humans were eager to leave their war-torn past behind and prove they were ready to join galactic civilization. There were mistakes and accidents, but their inclusion into the Federation was an overall success.

Humans are a source of pride for the Millennium Federation. What once was a race doomed to barbarism and endless war had elevated themselves to galactic society's highest ideals; and not through coercion or interference, but by example.

Today, not all Humans are eager to forget their history of warfare. While a great many would rather leave their violent past behind, there are others who not only cling to it, but claim it as their legacy. The most intense Galactic Defense drill sergeants, marines, and shock troopers are Humans. The most feared bounty hunters are Humans. The most vicious gangs and outlaws are all Humans (see: Black Hole Bill, Supernova Dragon Lords).

Despite the love affair many historians have with Humans, and the praise heaped upon them by the Millennium Federation for their undeniable progress, there are critics who refuse to see them as anything but barbarians too violent to be part of the Federation.

Now an ancient power from across the galaxy (see: the Star Power) has chosen a Human for its host. Is this a sign of the Humans' progress, or a dangerous weapon in the hands of killers?

The Zairakians are an organized people who thrive in a structured environment. They value law, order, and justice. They were one of the ten founding races of the Millennium Federation, a fact that many Zairakians are very proud of.

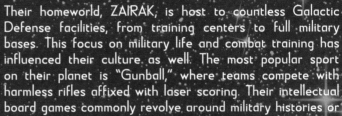

Of the original ten, commonly referred to as the Progenitors by Federation historians, it was the Zairakians' ideals that set the basis for law enforcement and social justice within the burgeoning planetary collective. Many Zairakians hold military service or law enforcement in high regard, as they see it as their responsibility to uphold the foundation of the galactic civilization they helped to form. It is said that there are more Zairakian officers in Galactic Defense than any other race in the Millennium Federation, and there are rumors of Zairakian families who have held such positions since the days of the Progenitors.

Their homeworld, ZAIRAK, is host to countless Galactic Defense facilities, from training centers to full military bases. This focus on military life and combat training has influenced their culture as well. The most popular sport on their planet is "Gunball," where teams compete with harmless rifles affixed with laser scoring. Their intellectual board games commonly revolve around military histories or diplomatic victories. It is also home to the Great Hall of Heroes (see below).

Their outspoken patriotism and combat prowess have brought out the best and worst of the Zairakians. The worst examples of their people have been military tyrants and ruthless overlords. The best examples have been crusaders for social justice, selfless soldiers on the battlefield, and "knights in shining armor" (see: Human expressions).

Among the worst in their history was General Fallan Kith, a merciless commander who took Zairakian pride too far. He believed in Zairakian superiority in all things, and saw the races joining the growing Federation as unworthy parasites. General Fallan led a separatist movement that was largely ignored at first, until his soldiers assaulted a number of Federation outposts belonging to other Progenitor races. The strikes were carried out with great military precision, and left no survivors. The Fallan Insurgency killed many in its genocidal crusade, until it was finally put down and General Fallan Kith was executed as one of the galaxy's greatest war criminals.

The best in their history is a list too great to count in mere words. Where General Fallan's name is spoken as a warning and in shame, the social activists and war heroes of the Zairakians are displayed in the Great Hall of Heroes on Zairak. It is a sprawling, grand building with interactive displays and detailed information on every great Zairakian, from galactic saviors to local icons. There is Gaira Dinn, who spoke for the embattled Adraxees; Motha Bant, who sacrificed herself to save her entire squadron from the Hazaikk Swarm; Banta Gilden, whose efforts stopped the Fallan Insurgency once and for all; the names go on and on.

Zairakians have a proud musical tradition as well. Their numerous fanfares and marches are among the most iconic in the Millennium Federation (see: Battle Hymn of the Gilden Knights, March of the Defenders). While traditional Zairakian music consists mostly of these military-themed songs, there is a growing interest in less structured themes. Younger Zairakians, inspired by the cultures of other races, have begun experimenting with improvisational styles. Nicknamed "jazzairak" by the Humans, it is a surprisingly free form of musical expression from the otherwise orderly Zairakians. The sensibilities of the older generation have been ruffled by this movement, but as long as their fanfares and marches remain untouched, they do not seem to mind.

They take fashion very seriously. From their traditional military-inspired garb to the chic styles of their cosmopolitan cities, Zairakians are careful with their appearance. Their zai and zei, nicknamed "mustaches" and "beards" by the Humans, are their most important feature in their fashion. Akin to Humans' obsession with their hair, Zairakian males style and sometimes dye their zai to make them more attractive, while females are known to enhance their zei with extensions, dyes, and the occasional surgery.

Zairakian pride is their greatest virtue, and their greatest flaw. They are hugely proud of their culture and accomplishments, take great care of their appearance, and are unwavering patriots of the Millennium Federation. To insult any of these things is a sure way to start a fight, but proud is the Zairakian who can exercise the self-discipline to walk away from a petty conflict.

Adraxees are a tall people with a long history of violence and crime. Their inclusion in the Millennium Federation was hotly debated, but they were ultimately given the opportunity to prove themselves. The gamble paid off, and galactic society gained one of the most loyal and passionate races among the thousand worlds.

Their homeworld, AXIOSIS, was plagued by crime before its assimilation. Pirates terrorized the skies. Drug lords preyed upon the young and the weak. Street gangs fought rivals over territory with innocents caught in the crossfire. Blood money bought the silence and blindness of the already struggling police force. The Adraxees longed for a change, and embraced the Millennium Federation with open arms.

The change was beneficial. While those same pirates, drug lords, and street gangs tried desperately to paint Galactic Defense as "invaders from beyond," the Adraxees soon realized they were there to bolster their native, struggling law enforcement and to protect those who could not protect themselves. Unsurprisingly, a great number of Adraxees joined Galactic Defense to take up arms against their outlaw oppressors.

Those who did not join Galactic Defense to battle their home's crime formed vigilante groups of their own, and the legal nature of these groups is still under fierce debate on Axiosis and beyond. Some are well-meaning and benevolent, like the Shield Saints, who unofficially guard less-regulated sections of cities; or the Sunrise Vagabonds, who patrol trade routes in search of pirate activity. Others are as violent and merciless as the criminals they hunt, like the Inquisitors, who often leave crime scenes of their own.

Their assimilation into the Millennium Federation also had an unexpected effect. Many criminals were quickly going from hunter to hunted, and many gave up the chase by simply straightening up their act and "going legit" (see: Human expressions). This worked marvelously to drop the crime rate, but it flooded the Adraxee work force with former outlaws. While a great many were honestly trying to turn their lives around, there were others who began working within these new laws to continue their unethical practices. This has made some people unwary of all Adraxee-run businesses.

Though criminal activity is still a very serious problem on Axiosis, it is at a fraction of its former influence. Some Adraxees still romanticize their pirates, drug lords, and street gangs as "independent spirits," but the majority remember them as brutal criminal rulers, and have not forgotten their tyranny.

Family is everything to an Adraxee, and this tradition not only extends to the other side of the law, but it thrives there. There are five major crime families on Axiosis, and for all their lawless behavior there are a number unwritten but highly-respected rules that govern how they interact with one another, and it revolves around familial respect and honor. Despite this code of conduct, they are far from "criminals with hearts of gold." Within those unwritten rules, there is still plenty of room for bloody revenge and vicious murders.

The Adraxee focus on family has caused number of problems for those who join Galactic Defense with relatives connected to the criminal underworld. Some Adraxees have gone so far as to sever ties with their outlaw kin and claim their new military comrades as "family." Galactic Defense squads that count an Adraxee among them know they have an unflinchingly loyal friend for life.

Their history of violence and suffering is expressed with eerie beauty in their music. Their most famous symphonies are choral dirges and requiems. Adraxee musicians have redefined what Humans called "the blues" (see: ancient Human music) into moving, sweeping songs of suffering, sorrow, and ultimately hope. More aggressive Adraxee music focuses on personal rage and loss, political corruption, and social injustice. Jazzairak has taken hold among the Adraxees, though it is often flavored with more mellow and somber themes. Upbeat songs certainly exist in their culture, but the most well-known Adraxee music is woven with their embattled history.

The traditional sport on Axiosis is Raxee, a tournament-style competition using the martial art for which the sport is named. Raxee makes great use of an Adraxee's long limbs, and a grand master is almost untouchable in melee combat. The most popular sport among Adraxees is Gunball, the Zairakian laser-scoring rifle game. Their styles of "combat" is a back-and-forth contest between orderly, textbook tactics and hit-and-run, guerilla warfare. Both sides have traded victories and championships, the makings of a rivalry for the ages.

The Shulentin are among the friendliest, most amicable people in the Millennium Federation. Their willingness to help and compassion for others have made them almost universally beloved. Their friendly reputation has become a shield of sorts. It is considered cowardly or especially brutish to harm one of them, as they are rarely violent themselves.

Their homeworld, SHULEN, is a truly communal place. Everything from food to currency is shared by all of its inhabitants. They have no centralized government, as they take it upon themselves to make certain their families, friends, neighbors, and strangers are happy and comfortable. Even parenting is a communal effort, and the concept of a single mother-and-father pair (beyond the male and female biological pairing required for conception) is truly alien to a Shulentin. Their community is their family, with their joys and sorrows to be shared with everyone.

Early contact with the Shulentin resulted in some strange but harmless misunderstandings. Shulentin communities would entrust Millennium Federation Frontier teams with their children, sometimes for days on end without explanation. Hungry Shulentin would simply pluck food from Frontier explorers without realizing they were "stealing." Shulentin would look on in horror as Frontier explorers, invited to a communal meal, would serve themselves first. But for every cultural misunderstanding, there was a cascade of apologies and a willingness to make up for the error on both sides.

Some early critics of the Shulentin accused them of being "too good to be true" and were convinced they were hiding some dark secret under the facade of their innocent, compassionate paradise. Centuries have proved those critics to be on the wrong side of history, as the Shulentin are truly what they appear to be: an innocent, compassionate people from a paradise world.

The Shulentin have tried to introduce their customs to other worlds, but with little success. They recognize the laws of the Millennium Federation are necessary for other races who do not possess their solidarity, and follow them out of respect for their new galactic allies.

The Shulentin have a very basic naming tradition. Females have "Shi" before their given names, while males have "Shu" before theirs. Further community distinctions are made by the patterns on their heads.

The Ladori are an amphibious, diverse people who are as known for their adaptability as they are for their cuisine. Many Humans perceived themselves as the most diverse and adaptable, until they met the Ladori. The two races became fast friends despite their unspoken rivalry.

Their homeworld, SOOLIIA, is home to sprawling cities built both above and below its vast, rolling oceans. Apoliiea, the planetary capital, attracts tourists from across the Millennium Federation seeking seafood prepared by some of the most renowned chefs in the galaxy.

As befitting a race born in the water, swimming is the most popular sport in their culture. Their annual championship, the Sooliia Aquaia, is one of the most-watched broadcast events in the Federation and is considered a holiday by many Ladori. "Aquaia-mania" is the commercial term for the month leading up to the great sporting event, which is a fascinating combination of swimming, diving, fishing, and competitive cooking.

The Ladori are prone to a curious genetic disorder from their past. Normally short in stature, there are some who grow to be as tall as an Adraxee, or even a Montodi. They are called the Ladora. They are superior physical specimens, often have intellects that rival the greatest thinkers of their generation, and live twice as long as a normal Ladori. However, when they reach early adulthood their minds shut down to a vegetative state. Their bodies are alive, but they are not living (see: Ladori Social Debates), and continue to age to the end of their long lives. Millennium Federation scientists have been working to cure the mental shutdown, or even awaken a comatose Ladora, but none have been successful.

Less cosmopolitan Ladori are known to be explorers, deep space pilots, and Galactic Defense soldiers. They will take any opportunity to test their natural adaptability, thirst for adventure, and passion for exotic foods.

The Scintillians were an advanced race of conquerors from the other side of the galaxy. Their civilization predated the earliest beginnings of the First Empire, until they traveled to the stars and threw themselves out of time.

Their home world is lost to ancient history, but the Scintillians subjugated all its other races and drained it of its natural resources. The unworthy slaves were left on their barren planet to rot while they traveled to a new system to save themselves. The Scintillians used their Wormhole Engines to travel at the speed of light to the nearest star. The resulting time dilation, which they called Timeless Space, left them ageless as they effectively traveled forward in time. After light years of travel, they discovered a burgeoning interplanetary civilization. They immediately invaded it, conquered it, and enslaved its people.

It became known as the First Wormhole Invasion.

The Scintillians were terrible and merciless. They pushed scientific progress in the name of invasion and war. They developed a method of interstellar travel without time dilation, and were thus able to conquer neighboring worlds with frightening ease. The First Wormhole flourished on the backs of countless slaves, who lived and died under their tyrannical rule.

But not every Scintillian was a brutal tyrant. There was a small group of radicals who sought to uplift the races and make them equals in the ever-expanding First Wormhole. They preached compassion and mercy, and saw the benefit of cooperation over subjugation. Most of these radicals were promptly hunted and executed. In a desperate move, one small radical cell infiltrated a top-secret project and stole the plans for a new weapon. Its original name is also lost to ancient history, but the radicals renamed it "The Star Power."

These radicals took the Star Power onto themselves and fought back against their own people. They were able to modify the Star Power to spread it among the enslaved races, giving power to the powerless. These radicals soon became an army, and the Star Powered Sentinels began their revolution. The ruling Scintillians, who had grown complacent from years of unchallenged rule, were taken completely off-guard. They were fought back to the edge of their own empire, and in a desperate move of their own, they reactivated their Wormhole Engines to escape into Timeless Space.

The Scintillians always returned, generations into the future. Each time they returned, they discovered their old slaves had progressed and advanced further and further, and that more of these "unworthy parasites" were Star Powered Sentinels. Each time they returned, they made efforts to reclaim the empire they believed was rightfully theirs. Each time they returned, they were forced back into Timeless Space by the Star Powered Sentinels.

The Wormhole Invasions were becoming less and less successful, until the Scintillians returned for the eighth time...

The Eighth Wormhole Invasion was the most devastating war ever fought.

Galactic civilization was at its height, but not at its most benevolent. Millions of worlds under the leadership of a galactic monarchy, made arrogant by hundreds of thousands of years of dominance. There was order, but not peace. Martial law was the order of the day, much to the suffering of the countless worlds. Even the Star Powered Sentinels, the former protectors of this sprawling civilization, were outgunned by the massive fleets of the Last Empire.

It was easy for the returning Scintillians to start a war when they arrived for the eighth time. They sowed the seeds of rebellion and terrorism. They had the technology to easily kill Star Powered Sentinels. So for the first time, instead of facing a galactic civilization alone, they recruited its own suffering people into their army. It was civil war on a terrible scale, and the "traitors" never knew that they were fighting to replace their merciless rulers with even worse tyrants.

And the Star Powered Sentinels were caught in the middle. Declared "enemies of the empire" for continuing to work against their totalitarian rule, and being the ancient enemies of the Scintillians, the well-meaning Sentinels were hunted by both sides. Technology was developed to track them anywhere. There was nowhere to go. Only a selfless handful survived to pass The Star Power on to a new generation of Sentinels after the war was over.

It lasted three centuries. Generations were born and died knowing only war. The death toll was uncountable. Entire planets were ruined by unthinkably destructive weapons. Civilizations with rich, storied histories were wiped out in moments. The Last Empire was ruined and the Eighth Wormhole was decimated. There was no winner, and it seemed civilization was doomed to sink into a Dark Age unlike any other.

However, on the far side of the galaxy, where the Last Empire had been looking to expand before the Eighth Wormhole, a spark of hope was slowly emerging...

ORIGINAL LITERAL STAR-POWERED DESIGN.

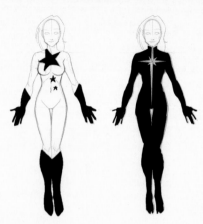

GARTH GRAHAM: I tried some "classic" emblem-style designs and knew immediately Michael could never see them. He'd love them too much.

QUICK SKETCH TO MAKE SURE THE COSTUME WOULDN'T LOOK TOTALLY RIDICULOUS ON A GUY.

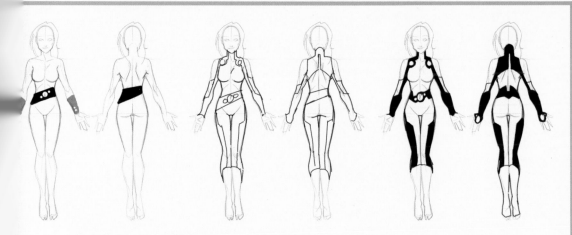

GARTH: It wasn't until I hit on the idea of an "orion's belt" that the design really started to take shape.

GARTH: Danica, herself came much quicker than her uniform. I knew I wanted her to be more "handsome" than "beautiful" so she got herself a strong heroic jawline, a razor sharp nose, and an athletic figure: strong arms, defined shoulders, killer calves. But Danica is not a super serious person, which is why she's drawn so often with that slightly lopsided, honest smile.

There are days that I totally want to change her hair. Half the time it looks awesome, and the rest it's just kinda awkward to draw. Which probably makes it all too genuine.

NO HERO IS COMPLETE WITHOUT SOME EXCELLENT VILLAINS FOR THEM TO RUN UP AGAINST.

GARTH: The Countess and Black Hole Bill are two characters that managed to survive the scuttling of the original Captain Space idea, largely unchanged. The Countess did become more regal and crazy-pants. I also apparently did an amazing thing and made her more alien with her bendy-flex Gumby limbs. I had totally forgotten that she was originally much more human-esque until Michael Reminded me I had originally drawn her with boobs. I'm really glad I changed that.

COUNTESS NURAK-NOR

COUNTESS HASA

HUMAN

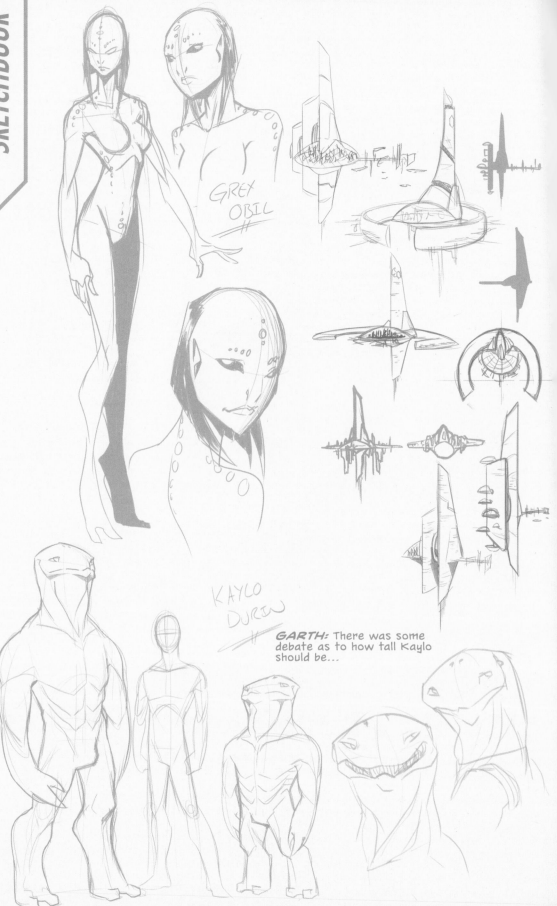

GREY OBIL

KAYLO DURIN

GARTH: There was some debate as to how tall Kaylo should be...

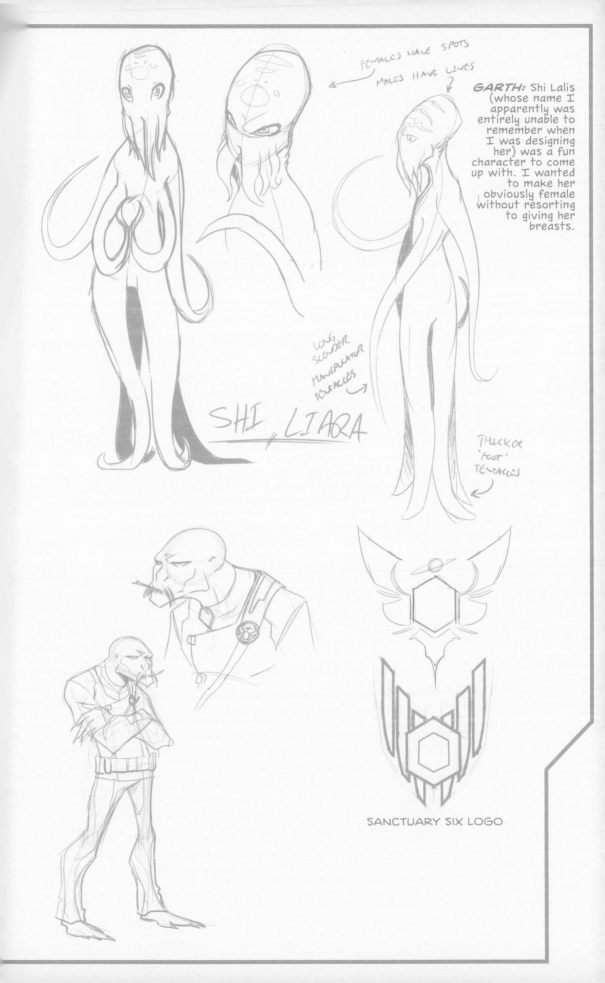

FEMALES HAVE SPOTS

MALES HAVE LINES

GARTH: Shi Lalis (whose name I apparently was entirely unable to remember when I was designing her) was a fun character to come up with. I wanted to make her obviously female without resorting to giving her breasts.

LONG SLENDER MANIPULATOR TENTACLES

SHI, LIARA

THICKER 'FOOT' TENTACLES

SANCTUARY SIX LOGO

NOT SAYING IT
WAS ALIENS...

LOVE HUMANITY
FOR TINY
HATS

4 LEGS

ALIEN
CAT
NEVER
BLINKS

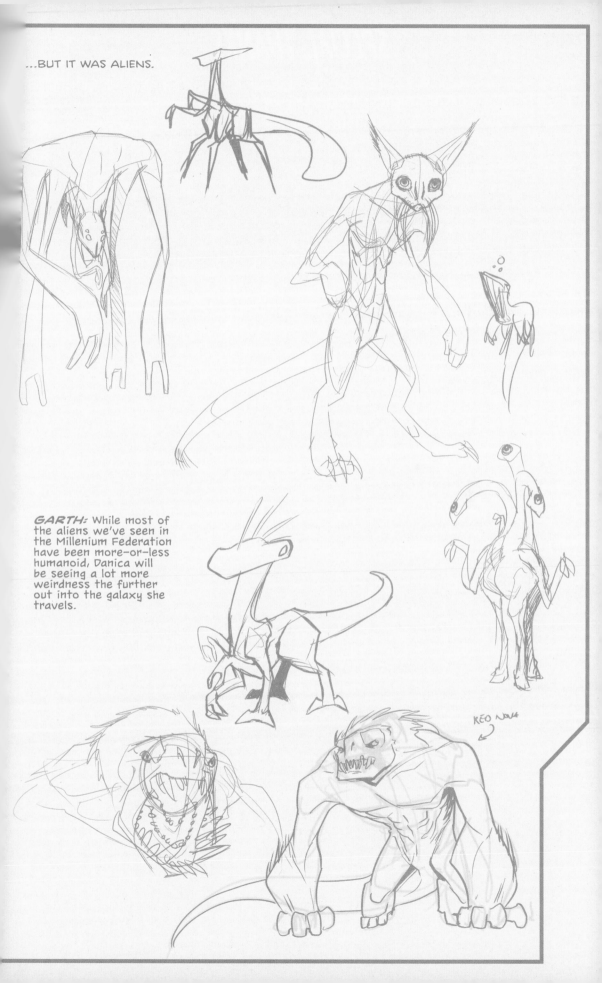

...BUT IT WAS ALIENS.

GARTH: While most of the aliens we've seen in the Millenium Federation have been more-or-less humanoid, Danica will be seeing a lot more weirdness the further out into the galaxy she travels.

REO NOVA

SPECIAL THANKS

THIS BOOK WAS MADE POSSIBLE WITH THE HELP OF KICKSTARTER AND THE GENEROUS CONTRIBUTIONS OF THE FOLLOWING SENTIENT BEINGS:

A Marshall
Aaron Edens
Aaron Gann
Aaron R Corff
Aaron Sofaer
Aaron Westphal
Accalia Elementia
Adam Andrzejczak
Adam Brancato
Adam Conner
Adam Van Wyk
Adrian Tymes
Adrienne Ng
Afroshin
AJ Medder
Al Mayse
Al Sparrow
Alan Bradshaw
Alan Conlon
Alec Zale
Alex
Alex Heberling
Alex Lilley
Alex Matthews
Alex Peake
Alexander Kubricka
Alexander Sanner
Alexander Withey
Alfonso E Martinez III
Allan Mills
Allison Hill
Ally Hisle
Amanda Kedaigle
Amber Yust
Amy Briggs
Amy Wagstaff-Weston
Ana King
Anarelton
Anastasiya Shvarts
Andrea Calogera (EFG)
Andreas
Andreas Woetzold
Andrew Elliott
Andrew Farr
Andrew Gwynn
Andrew Ihla
Andrew Konopacki
Andrew Laliberte
Andrew LaLonde
Andrew Martin
Andy Hartshorn
Andy Herrman
Ann-Kathrin
Anon
Anthony Ricgards
Antonio Rodriguez
Antti Hallamäki
ao2l
Ash Maxfield
Ashley Burden
Ashley Oswald
Ashley Rodriguez
Athan
Austin Wardwa
B. Haas
B.Link
Barbara Ehleh
Barbara Johnson-Haddad
Barbara Leicher
Barry Holmes
Beatrice Matarazzo
Beausabre
Ben Cush
Ben Hofmann
Ben Jenkinson

Ben Knuchel
Ben the Pyrate
Ben Valvano
Ben Vara
Benjamin Cooner
Benjamin Rodrique
Benjamin Schollnick
Bernhard Stomporowski
Billy Poggi
Bob & Kate
Bobby Skeens
Bombril
Boojum the brown bunny
Brad Dunlap
Brandon Scott Robertson
Brendan Hencher
Brennan See
Brett Daniel
Brewe
Brian Day
Brian Griffin
Brian James
Brian Ray
Brian, Sarah, & Josh Williams
Bridie Doherty
Britny Musson
Bryan Blackburn
Bryant Cable
C. Cole
Caitlin Stumpf
Carl Brost
Carl Kerschner
Carrie Browne
Casey Townsend
Cassandra Brindle
Chad Jarvis
Chaddaï
Charis Papavassilis
Charles Petersen
Charles Timko
Chayde
Cheshi
Chris
Chris Abernethy
Chris Arnold
Chris Cordell
Chris Cottam
Chris Dryden
Chris Fong
Chris Leth
Chris Manvell
Chris Shumway
Chris W
Christian B
Christian Bork Jessen
Christian Engelund
Christine Anderson
Christopher C. Cockrell
Christopher Colton
Christopher Courtney
Christopher Kelley
Christopher Pelletier
Chuck Reuse
Claire Boswell
Clint Leetwood
Cole Hurley
Coniah Grimes
Connie Elliott
Connor Tee
Conrad "Lynx" Wong
Corbin Staaben
Cordell Finnson
Cost2kilu
Coyote Camouflage
Craig Blackwood

Craig Maquet
Cristin Davis
Crow Crowther
Cryolite
Crystal M Rollins
GSW
CtrlAltFaceroll
Curtis Callaway
D-Rock
Dallin & Janie Edvalson
Damian Cheung
Dampel Illandra
Dan & Rachel Smith
Dan Garated
Dan Gibson
Dan Warner
Dana McVey
Daniel
Daniel Bartholomew
Daniel Blake
Daniel Butterworth
Daniel Fritzel
Daniel Lin
Daniel Reising
Daniel Walker Woodward
Daria McGinnis
Darren Popik
Darryl Smith
Dave A
David
David "SlyDave" Gray
David "Yoda" Odie
David Abplanalp
David Bellinger
David Chuhay
David Conrad
David Dryden
David Glass
David Glennie (Taint)
David Jones
David Miller
David Raynaud
David Ross Hardy
David Sanford
Davyd Titze
Dawn Chester
DDC2OXL
Declan O'Connell
Del Eury
Dennys Antunish
Derek Outwater
Derek Song
Dick Neal
Dimitri
DivineWrath
Dominic Quach
Doris Gimarie Battle
Douglas Reid
Douglas Shepard
Dr. Jammin
Dr. Kopong T. Limson
Dr. Stefanie H. Chen
Dragon Treviño
Durmroenark
Dylan Royston
E the Weasel
Edward Leal
Efren Rodriguez
Elaugaufein
Elciram
Eli Horowitz
Eli Pailet
Elise Francoeur
Elizabeth Burgess
Elizabeth Goodwill

Emil Scott
Emmanuel Lapierre
Eric "ogehn" Brenders
Eric Andres
Eric Daniel
Eric Guerber
Eric Huffman
Eric Menge
Eric Moore
Eric Scott Seybert
Eric Sigler
Eric Silvia
Erik
Erik Harpstead
Erik Lawther
Erik Silva
Erik Fr
Esh Lerch
Ethan & Lori Hattendorf
Ethan Prosen
Ethan Sebasco
Etienne-Donzelot
Exastiken
Fabstar01000101
Fahad Naeem
Firab ul Kron
Fiona Erasmuson
Florian Gillard
Florian Graf
Florian J
Forrest Jungck
Frank Kim
Fuzzy Duck
Gabe Dartt
Gabriel Poole
Gadareth
Garrett Muggy
Gavin Riches
Geoffrey Adams
Geoffrey Hebel
Georgieanna
Giacomo Maria Bacchelli
Gordon Gillespie
Grant Ah Shay
Gray Detrick
Gregory Hite
Gregory Seidman
Greta Sayle
HAILTOTHEVOID
Haisyn Fierra
HAL1800
Hannah
Hanne Van de Beek
Heidi Sosinski
Henrik Stentärn
Henry & Victoria
Hoyt Dat
Hunter A Steele
Hunter Evensten
Ian Castruita
Ilana J Sprongl
Ilearch n'n'daCorna
Ivar Sintemaartensdijk
J & K Walker
J C Locke
J. W. Bennett
Jacob M Durrant
Jacob Pawson
Jacob VanTol
JAK
Jakob Haas
James
James Conason
James Edward Reed
James Flaagan

James Harris
James Heffron
James Meehan
James Monty-Carbonari
James Moss
Jan Meiners
Jason Higgins
Jason Howson
Jason Mullikin
Jason Rice
Jason T. Forde [Monkey No.5 in Sp
Jax
Jay Bandoy
Jaybles
Jeff Sweeney
Jeff Williams
Jeffery Lawler
Jen & Eric Desmarais
Jen Pawley
Jennifer Jones
Jennifer McGoffey
Jennifer Thomas
Jennifer Zyren Smith
Jens Bejer Pedersen
Jeremiah Dupont
Jeremy Kear
Jeremy Mitchell
Jeremy Stoa
Jeroen Stoker
Jesse Hackett
Jesse Ozog
Jesse Rizutko
Jesse Varga
Jessica Gadling
Jessica Mugelmer
JF Quensel
Jim
Jim Gould
Jim Haas aka Nate the Robo
Jim Martin
Jim Millican
Jo "TheNobleOne" N
Jo Ellen Vallee
Joe
Joe "Hex" Leggart
Joe Mendiola
Joe Murphy
Joe Rundin
Joel "Ikkorous" Chapman
Joel Wismer
Joey STANFORD
John Bartley
John Burnham
John D. Barr
John Irvine
John J Ostropsky Jr.
John J. Allen III
John MacLeod
John Mullis
JoJo Seames
Jon Hoque
Jon Russell
Jonathan "ChessboardMan" Barrett
Jonathan Boynton
Jonathan East
Jonathan Finke
Jonathan Guagenti
Jonathan Hairston
Jonathan Pestana
Jonathan Spaulding
Jordan Harding
Jörg Tremmel
Jose E Mendez
Jose Luis Perez Zapata
Joseph Andelman

THE STAR POWERED ADVENTURES OF DANICA MARIS CONTINUE ONLINE

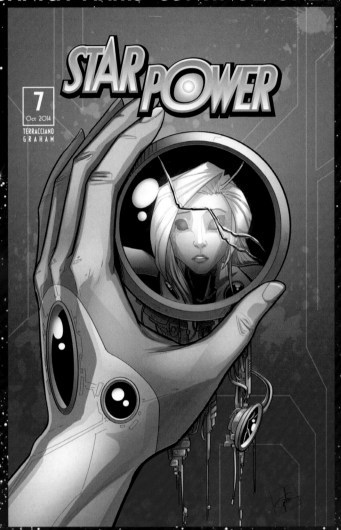

STARPOWERCOMIC.COM